Guest Spot

Playalong for Saxophone
ALL NEW CHART HITS

Wise Publications
part of The Music Sales Group
LONDON / NEW YORK / PARIS / SYDNEY / COPENHAGEN / BERLIN / MADRID / HONG KONG / TOKYO

Published by
Wise Publications
14-15 Berners Street, London W1T 3LJ, UK.

Exclusive Distributors:
Music Sales Limited
Distribution Centre, Newmarket Road, Bury St Edmunds,
Suffolk IP33 3YB, UK.
Music Sales Pty Limited
20 Resolution Drive, Caringbah, NSW 2229, Australia.

Order No. AM1004058
ISBN 13: 978-1-78038-360-6
This book © Copyright 2011 Wise Publications,
a division of Music Sales Limited.

Edited by Jenni Norey.
Engraving and arranging supplied by Camden Music.
Top line arrangements by Christopher Hussey.
Backing tracks by Danny Gluckstein, Jeff Leach and John Maul.
Saxaphone played by Howard McGill.
CD recorded, mixed and mastered by Jonas Persson.

Printed in the EU.

Your Guarantee of Quality:
As publishers, we strive to produce every book to
the highest commercial standards.
The music has been freshly engraved and the book has been
carefully designed to minimise awkward page turns and
to make playing from it a real pleasure.
Particular care has been given to specifying acid-free, neutral-sized
paper made from pulps which have not been elemental chlorine bleached.
This pulp is from farmed sustainable forests and was
produced with special regard for the environment.
Throughout, the printing and binding have been planned to
ensure a sturdy, attractive publication which should give years of enjoyment.
If your copy fails to meet our high standards,
please inform us and we will gladly replace it.

www.musicsales.com

LIGATURE

MOUTHPIECE

CROOK

THUMB SUPPORT

BODY

1L

4L

2L
3L
1ST FINGER

5L
2ND FINGER
3RD FINGER
6L
7L
8L
9L

LEFT HAND

OCTAVE KEY

THUMB REST

RIGHT HAND

1R

2R

3R

*4R

1ST FINGER

5R
2ND FINGER

3RD FINGER
6R

7R

THE RING

* Not fitted on some saxophones

Saxophone Fingering Chart

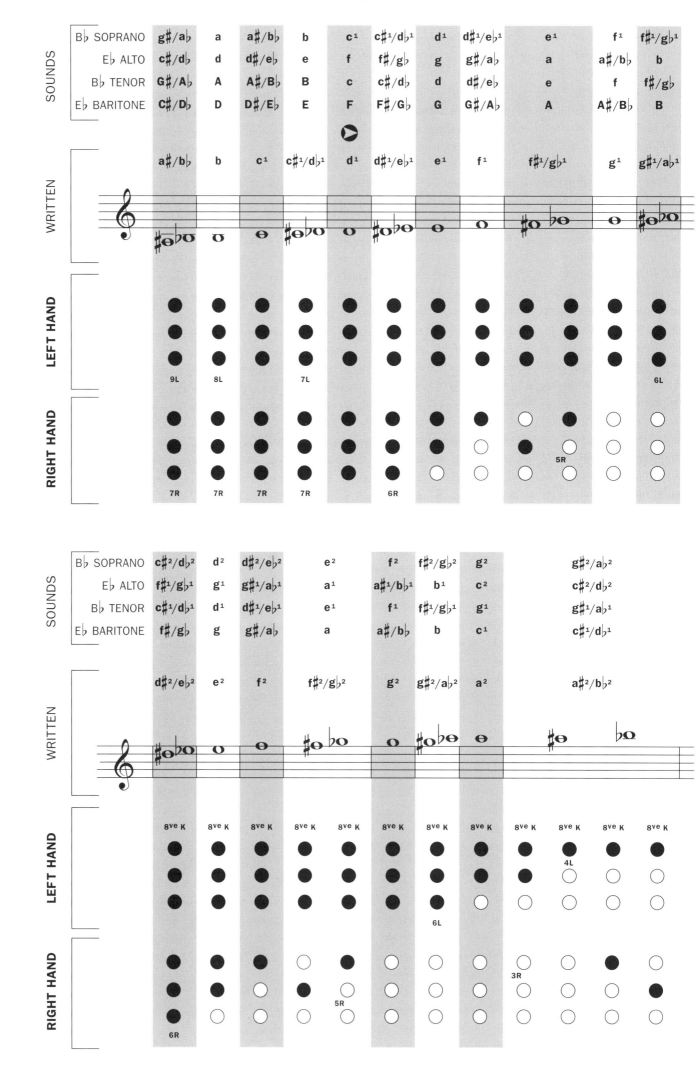

Indicates the lower limit of the best playing range

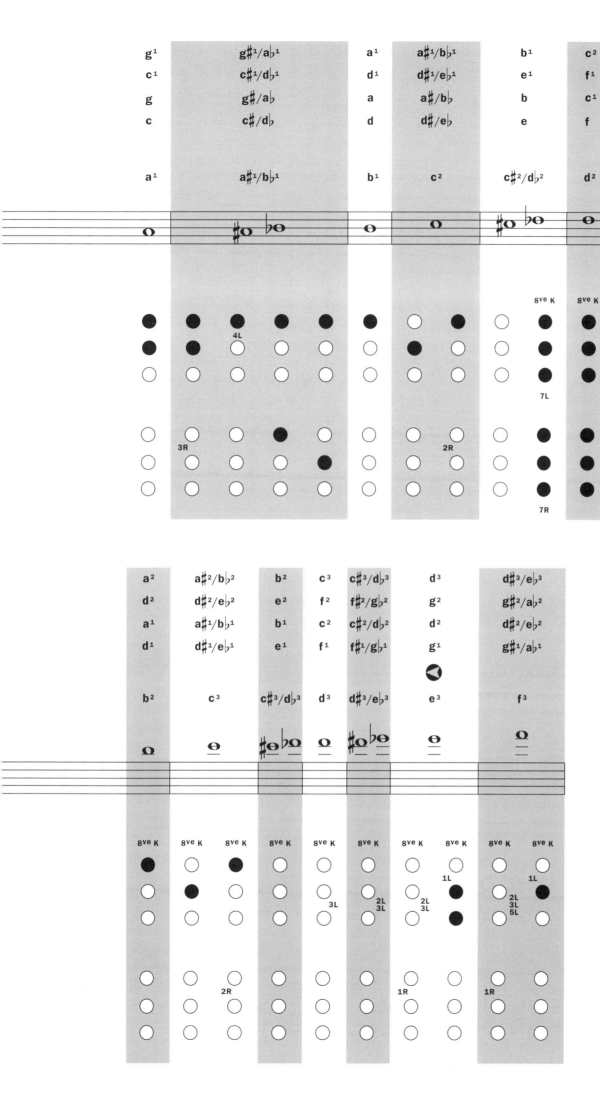

Indicates the upper limit of the best playing range

All About Tonight (Pixie Lott)

Words & Music by Brian Kidd, Thomas James & Tebey Ottoh

The A Team (Ed Sheeran)

Words & Music by Ed Sheeran

Leisurely and simply ♩ = 85

Every Teardrop Is A Waterfall (Coldplay)

Words & Music by Chris Martin, Guy Berryman, Jon Buckland, Willl Champion, Brian Eno

Glad You Came (The Wanted)

Words & Music by Wayne Hector, Steve Mac & Ed Drewett

Grenade (Bruno Mars)

Words & Music by Philip Lawrence, Peter Hernandez, Christopher Brown, Ari Levine, Claude Kelly & Andrew Wyatt

6/16.

Expressively ♩ = 111

(hi-hat cue)   *mp*

mf

f

Jar Of Hearts (Christina Perri)

Words & Music by Christina Perri, Drew Lawrence & Barrett Yeretsian

Last Friday Night (Katy Perry)

Words & Music by Max Martin, Lukasz Gottwald, Bonnie McKee & Katy Perry

Confidently ♩ = 126

Love Goes Down (Plan B)

Words & Music by Benjamin Drew, Eric Appapoulay, Richard Cassell & Tom Goss

Jealousy (Will Young)

Words & Music by Will Young, James Eliot & Jemima Stilwell

Tenderly ♩ = 123

Someone Like You (Adele)

Words & Music by Adele Adkins & Daniel Wilson

Smoothly, with tenderness ♩ = 68

mp espressivo

mf

poco cresc.

mp   *p*

CD Track Listing

Full instrumental performances...

1. Tuning notes
2. All About Tonight
   (Kidd/James/Ottoh) Universal/MCA Music Limited/
   BMG Rights Management (UK) Limited/Copyright Control
3. The A Team
   (Sheeran) Sony/ATV Music Publishing (UK) Limited
4. Every Teardrop Is A Waterfall
   (Martin/Berryman/Buckland/Champion/Eno/Allen/Anderson/Castioni/
   Christensen/Lagonda/Wycombe)
   Harry Castioni/Alex Joerg Christensen/B Lagonda/Wycombe/Opal Music/
   Universal Music Publishing Limited/Universal Music Publishing MGB Limited/
   Warner/Chappell Overseas Holdings Limited
5. Glad You Came
   (Hector/Mac/Drewett)
   Warner/Chappell Music Publishing Limited/Peermusic (UK) Limited
6. Grenade
   (Lawrence/Hernandez/Brown/Levine/Kelly/Wyatt)
   Sony/ATV Music Publishing (UK) Limited/Warner/Chappell Music North
   America Limited/Bug Music (Windswept Account)/EMI Music Publishing Ltd/
   Bug Music Ltd
7. Jar Of Hearts
   (Perri/Lawrence/Yeretsian) Wixen Music UK Ltd/Warner/Chappell North
   America Limited/Fintage Publishing B.V.
8. Last Friday Night
   (Martin/Gottwald/McKee/Perry) Kobalt Music Publishing Limited/
   Warner/Chappell North America Limited/Kassner Associated Publishers Limited
9. Love Goes Down
   (Drew/Appapoulay/Cassell/Goss) Universal Music Publishing PGM Limited/
   Sony/ATV Music Publishing (UK) Limited
10. Jealousy
    (Young/Eliot/Stilwell) Sony/ATV Music Publishing (UK) Limited
11. Someone Like You
    (Adkins/Wilson) Universal Music Publishing Limited/Chrysalis Music Limited

Backing tracks only...

12. All About Tonight
13. The A Team
14. Every Teardrop Is A Waterfall
15. Glad You Came
16. Grenade
17. Jar Of Hearts
18. Last Friday Night
19. Love Goes Down
20. Jealousy
21. Someone Like You

MCPS

To remove your CD from the plastic sleeve,
lift the small lip to break the perforations.
Replace the disc after use for convenient storage